FOLENS MATHS
WEEKLY ASSESSMENT

Book 2

Hilary Koll

Steve Mills

Folens
Publishers

Introduction

Weekly Assessment and the National Numeracy Framework

Each of the six books in this series provides 34 sharply focused assessments that address the Year's National Numeracy Framework learning objectives. They are arranged in accordance with the five divisions of each yearly teaching programme, and will help teachers to review and record the progress children are making in relation to the learning objectives during each year of school.

The assessments

Assessments consist of either written questions or a mix of written and orally delivered questions, depending on the nature of the objectives. In both cases, the format ensures quick and easy marking.

Assessment administration

Each assessment will take approximately 20–30 minutes of class time, and might follow or conclude the final Mathematics session of the week. Assessments should be selected according to what has been taught in the week. Where an assessment includes oral questions it is recommended that these are delivered at the start and that no more than 5 seconds are given for each question.

Each assessment consists of two pages – a teacher page and a pupil page.

The teacher page includes:

● a list of the learning objectives in a division of the yearly teaching programme to provide overall context, together with the specific objectives assessed in the test (highlighted in bold type) and the related question numbers

● teacher notes that point out typical misconceptions and errors and also offer teaching tips

● oral questions for those tests that include oral work

● answers.

The pupil page is a page with questions and space for answers.

In addition, there is a photocopiable record sheet provided to allow you to record weekly assessment marks for all pupils.

Acknowledgements

Folens allows photocopying of pages marked 'copiable page' for educational use, providing that this use is within the confines of the purchasing institution. Copiable pages should not be declared in any return in respect of any photocopying licence.

Folens books are protected by international copyright laws. All rights are reserved. The copyright of all materials in this book, except where otherwise stated, remains the property of the publisher and authors. No part of this publication may be reproduced, stored in a retrieval system, or transmitted, in any form or by any means, for whatever purpose, without the written permission of Folens Limited.

Hilary Koll and Steve Mills hereby assert their moral rights to be identified as the authors of this work in accordance with the Copyright, Designs and Patents Act 1988.

Editor: Hayley Willer   Layout artist: Philippa Jarvis
Cover design: Ed Gallagher   Illustrations: Susan Hutchison
Cover photograph: Kelvin Freeman (With thanks to Grove Park Primary School, Chiswick.)

© 1999 Folens Limited, on behalf of the authors.

Summary of teaching programme objectives from the *Framework for Teaching Mathematics*, published by the DfEE as part of the National Numeracy Strategy.

First published 1999 by Folens Limited, Dunstable and Dublin.

Folens Limited, Albert House, Apex Business Centre, Boscombe Road, Dunstable, LU5 4RL, United Kingdom. Reprinted 2000.

ISBN 186202 823–0

Printed in Singapore by Craft Print.

Contents

ASSESSMENT 1 Counting, properties of numbers and number sequences

Activity sheet questions

Oral
1–10 ● Say the number names in order to at least 100, from and back to zero.
Written
1 ● Count reliably up to 100 objects by grouping them: for example, in tens, then in fives or twos.
2 ● Describe and extend simple number sequences:
    – **count on or back in ones or tens, starting from any two-digit number**
    – count in hundreds from and back to zero
    – count on in twos from and back to zero or any small number, and recognise odd and even numbers to at least 30
    – count on in steps of 3, 4 or 5 to at least 30, from and back to zero, then from and back to any given small number.
● Begin to recognise two-digit multiples of 2, 5 or 10.

Teacher note

● Children should understand cardinality, i.e. the number of items in a set is given by the last number in the count.

Oral questions

1. Which number comes *after* 34?
2. Which number comes *after* 57?
3. Which number comes *before* 92?
4. Which number comes *before* 100?
5. Which tens number comes *after* 20?
6. Which tens number comes *after* 40?
7. Which tens number comes *before* 70?
8. Which tens number comes *after* 90?
9. Which hundreds number comes *after* 300?
10. Which hundreds number comes *after* 900?

Answers

1.	**35**	6.	**50**
2.	**58**	7.	**60**
3.	**91**	8.	**100**
4.	**99**	9.	**400**
5.	**30**	10.	**1000**

1   a. How many stars are there?   b. How many counters are there?

37		51

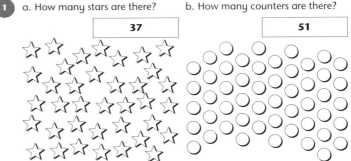

2   Write the next two numbers in the train carriages.

a.

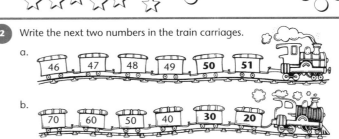

46   47   48   49   **50**   **51**

b.

70   60   50   40   **30**   **20**

Name: _____   Date: _____

1.	6.
2.	7.
3.	8.
4.	9.
5.	10.

1 a. How many stars are there?   b. How many counters are there?

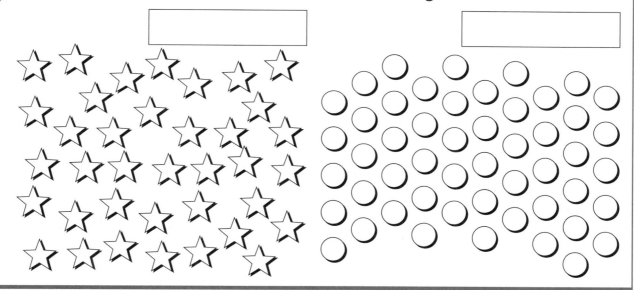

2 Write the next two numbers in the train carriages.

a.

| 46 | 47 | 48 | 49 | | |

b.

| 70 | 60 | 50 | 40 | | |

Activity sheet questions

- Say the number names in order to at least 100, from and back to zero.
- Count reliably up to 100 objects by grouping them: for example, in tens, then in fives or twos.

Oral 1–10 & Written 1–4

- Describe and extend simple number sequences:
  - **count on or back in ones or tens, starting from any two-digit number**
  - count in hundreds from and back to zero
  - count on in twos from and back to zero or any small number, and recognise odd and even numbers to at least 30
  - count on in steps of 3, 4 or 5 to at least 30, from and back to zero, then from and back to any given small number.
- Begin to recognise two-digit multiples of 2, 5 or 10.

Teacher note

- Children need to understand the ordinality of numbers to enable them to position items in a set. There will need to be plenty of opportunity for children to count out loud in the class and to order items using both 'one, two, three', and 'first, second, third'. The use of number rhymes can help children to learn the rhythms of counting.

Oral questions

Write the number that comes next.
1. 51, 52 …
2. 88, 89 …
3. 43, 42 …
4. 71, 70 …
5. Count on 4 from 35.
6. Count on 5 from 46.
7. Count back 5 from 67.
8. Count back 6 from 54.
9. Count on from 46 to 53. How many did you count?
10. Count back from 84 to 79. How many did you count?

Answers

1.	**53**	6.	**51**
2.	**90**	7.	**62**
3.	**41**	8.	**48**
4.	**69**	9.	**7**
5.	**39**	10.	**5**

1 Here is part of a number line. Fill in the missing numbers.

20	21	22	23	24	25	26	27	28	29

2 Write the missing numbers.

48	49	50	51	52	53	54	55

3 Here is part of a number line. Fill in the missing numbers.

10	20	30	40	50	60	70	80	90	100

4 Write the missing numbers.

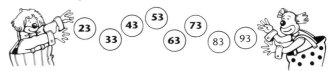

23 33 43 53 63 73 83 93

Name: _____ Date: _____

2 Counting, properties of numbers and number sequences

1.	6.
2.	7.
3.	8.
4.	9.
5.	10.

1 Here is part of a number line. Fill in the missing numbers.

			23	24	25				

2 Write the missing numbers.

51 52

3 Here is part of a number line. Fill in the missing numbers.

			40	50	60				

4 Write the missing numbers.

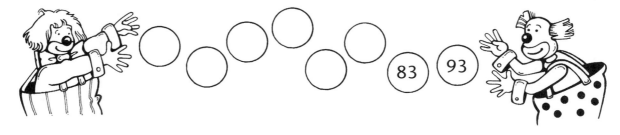

83 93

MATHS WEEKLY ASSESSMENT: *Book 2*

Activity sheet questions

- Say the number names in order to at least 100, from and back to zero.
- Count reliably up to 100 objects by grouping them: for example, in tens, then in fives or twos.
- Describe and extend simple number sequences:
  - count on or back in ones or tens, starting from any two-digit number

Written

1 – **count in hundreds from and back to zero**

2–3 – **count on in twos from and back to zero or any small number**

4–6 – **recognise odd and even numbers to at least 30**

  - count on in steps of 3, 4 or 5 to at least 30, from and back to zero, then from and back to any given small number.
- Begin to recognise two-digit multiples of 2, 5 or 10.

Teacher note

- Children need to understand that it is the units digit that determines whether a number is odd or even, however large the number.

Answers

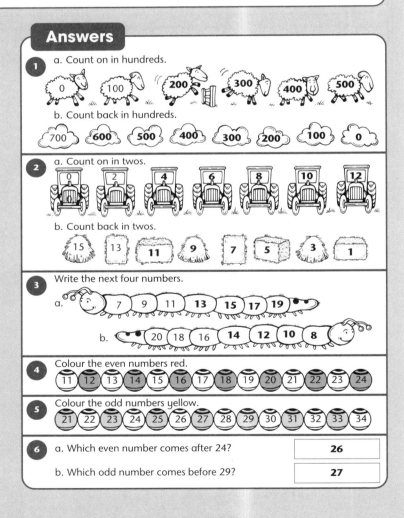

1

a. Count on in hundreds.
0, 100, 200, 300, 400, 500

b. Count back in hundreds.
700, 600, 500, 400, 300, 200, 100, 0

2

a. Count on in twos.
0, 2, 4, 6, 8, 10, 12

b. Count back in twos.
15, 13, **11**, 9, 7, 5, **3**, 1

3 Write the next four numbers.

a. 7, 9, 11, **13**, **15**, **17**, **19**

b. 20, 18, 16, **14**, **12**, **10**, **8**

4 Colour the even numbers red.
11, **12**, 13, **14**, 15, **16**, 17, **18**, 19, **20**, 21, **22**, 23, **24**

5 Colour the odd numbers yellow.
21, 22, **23**, 24, **25**, 26, **27**, 28, **29**, 30, **31**, 32, **33**, 34

6

a. Which even number comes after 24? | **26**

b. Which odd number comes before 29? | **27**

Name: _____   Date: _____

3 Counting, properties of numbers and number sequences

1 a. Count on in hundreds.

0   100

b. Count back in hundreds.

700

2 a. Count on in twos.

0   2

b. Count back in twos.

15   13

3 Write the next four numbers.

a. 7 9 11

b. 20 18 16

4 Colour the even numbers red.

11 12 13 14 15 16 17 18 19 20 21 22 23 24

5 Colour the odd numbers yellow.

21 22 23 24 25 26 27 28 29 30 31 32 33 34

6 a. Which even number comes after 24?

b. Which odd number comes before 29?

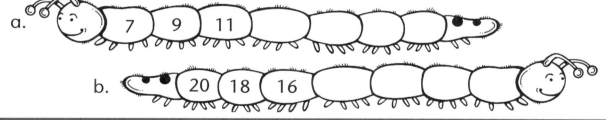

Activity sheet questions

- Say the number names in order to at least 100, from and back to zero.
- Count reliably up to 100 objects by grouping them: for example, in tens, then in fives or twos.
- Describe and extend simple number sequences:
  - count on or back in ones or tens, starting from any two-digit number
  - count in hundreds from and back to zero
  - count on in twos from and back to zero or any small number, and recognise odd and even numbers to at least 30

Oral 1–10 & Written 1 – **count on in steps of 3, 4 or 5 to at least 30, from and back to zero, then from and back to any given small number.**

2–4 ● **Begin to recognise two-digit multiples of 2, 5 or 10.**

Teacher note

- Children need to understand the ordinality of numbers to enable them to position items in a set. There will need to be plenty of opportunity for children to count out loud in the class and to order items using both 'one, two, three', and 'first, second, third'. The use of number rhymes can help children to learn the rhythms of counting.

Oral questions

Count on in threes in your head as I clap my hands. Write down the number we stop at.

1. '0, 3, 6 … clap, clap, clap.'
2. '17, 20 … clap, clap, clap.'

Count back in threes in your head as I clap my hands. Write down the number we stop at.

3. '32, 29 … clap, clap, clap.'

Count on in fours in your head as I clap my hands. Write down the number we stop at.

4. '4, 8 … clap, clap, clap.'
5. '18, 22 … clap, clap, clap, clap, clap.'

Count back in fours in your head as I clap my hands. Write down the number we stop at.

6. '28, 24 … … clap, clap, clap, clap.'

Now we will count in fives. Write the next two numbers.

7. 5, 10, 15 …   **9.** 25, 20 …
8. 22, 27 …   **10.** 41, 36 …

Answers

1. **15**	6. **8**
2. **29**	7. **20, 25**
3. **20**	8. **32, 37**
4. **20**	9. **15, 10**
5. **42**	10. **31, 26**

1 Fill in the missing numbers.

a. 22 — 25 — 28 — **31** — **34** — **37**

b. 29 — 25 — 21 — **17** — **13** — **9**

c. 13 — 18 — 23 — **28** — **33** — **38**

d. 37 — 32 — 27 — **22** — **17** — **12**

2 Draw circles around any multiples of 2.
② ⑥ ⑩ 15 17 ⑳ ㉔ ㉚

3 Draw circles around any multiples of 5.
14 ⑮ 18 ⑤ 9 ⑩ ㉚ ㉕

4 Draw circles around any multiples of 10.
27 ⑧⓪ ④⓪ ⑩⓪ 25 ⑩ 66 ⑨⓪

Name: _____   Date: _____

1.	6.
2.	7.
3.	8.
4.	9.
5.	10.

1 Fill in the missing numbers.

a. 22 — 25 — 28 — ◯ — ◯ — ◯

b. 29 — 25 — 21 — ◯ — ◯ — ◯

c. 13 — 18 — 23 — ◯ — ◯ — ◯

d. 37 — 32 — 27 — ◯ — ◯ — ◯

2 Draw circles around any multiples of 2.

2   6   10   15   17   20   24   30

3 Draw circles around any multiples of 5.

14   15   18   5   9   10   30   25

4 Draw circles around any multiples of 10.

27   80   40   100   25   10   66   90

Place value and ordering

Activity sheet questions

Oral
1–10 • Read and write whole numbers to at least 100 in figures and words.
Written
1–2 • Know what each digit in a two-digit number represents, including 0 as a place holder.

3 Use the = sign to represent equality.
Partition two-digit numbers into a multiple of ten and ones (TU).

• Use and begin to read the vocabulary of comparing and ordering numbers, including ordinal numbers to 100.
Compare two given two-digit numbers, say which is more or less, and give a number which lies between them.

• Say the number that is 1 or 10 more or less than any given two-digit number.

• Order whole numbers to at least 100, and position them on a number line and 100 square.

Teacher note

• Children may be familiar with the terms 'units' or 'ones'. Both are acceptable terms.

Oral questions

Write these numbers in figures.
1. Nine
2. Fifteen
3. Eighteen
4. Twenty-six
5. Forty
6. Fifty-three
7. Sixty-one
8. Seventy-six
9. Ninety-four
10. One hundred

Answers

1. **9**		6. **53**
2. **15**		7. **61**
3. **18**		8. **76**
4. **26**		9. **94**
5. **40**		10. **100**

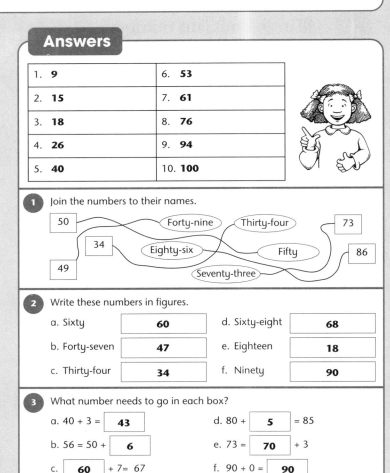

1 Join the numbers to their names.

50   Forty-nine   Thirty-four   73
    34   Eighty-six   Fifty   86
    49   Seventy-three

2 Write these numbers in figures.
a. Sixty **60**   d. Sixty-eight **68**
b. Forty-seven **47**   e. Eighteen **18**
c. Thirty-four **34**   f. Ninety **90**

3 What number needs to go in each box?
a. 40 + 3 = **43**   d. 80 + **5** = 85
b. 56 = 50 + **6**   e. 73 = **70** + 3
c. **60** + 7 = 67   f. 90 + 0 = **90**

Name: _____ Date: _____

1.	6.
2.	7.
3.	8.
4.	9.
5.	10.

1 Join the numbers to their names.

50   (Forty-nine)   (Thirty-four)   73

34   (Eighty-six)   (Fifty)   86

49   (Seventy-three)

2 Write these numbers in figures.

a. Sixty [   ]   d. Sixty-eight [   ]

b. Forty-seven [   ]   e. Eighteen [   ]

c. Thirty-four [   ]   f. Ninety [   ]

3 What number needs to go in each box?

a. 40 + 3 = [   ]   d. 80 + [   ] = 85

b. 56 = 50 + [   ]   e. 73 = [   ] + 3

c. [   ] + 7 = 67   f. 90 + 0 = [   ]

Place value and ordering

6
ASSESSMENT

Activity sheet questions

Written 1–6

- Read and write whole numbers to at least 100 in figures and words.
- **Know what each digit in a two-digit number represents, including 0 as a place holder, and partition two-digit numbers into a multiple of ten and ones (TU).**
- Use and begin to read the vocabulary of comparing and ordering numbers, including ordinal numbers to 100.
  Use the = sign to represent equality.
  Compare two given two-digit numbers, say which is more or less, and give a number which lies between them.
- Say the number that is 1 or 10 more or less than any given two-digit number.
- Order whole numbers to at least 100, and position them on a number line and 100 square.

Teacher note

- It is useful for children to have place-value cards to assist them with partitioning tens and ones (units). The use of 10 and 1 pence coins can also be useful in showing the value of each digit – the tens digit represents how many 10 pence coins there are, and the ones or units digit represents how many 1 pence coins there are. Children should also have experience of vertical abacuses as representations of two-digit numbers at this stage.
- Children may be familiar with the terms 'units' or 'ones'. Both are acceptable terms.

Answers

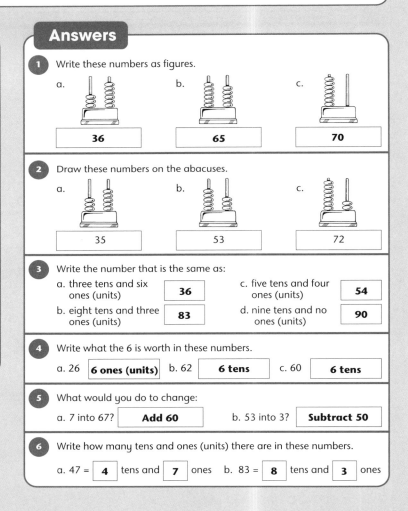

1 Write these numbers as figures.

a. **36** b. **65** c. **70**

2 Draw these numbers on the abacuses.

a. **35** b. **53** c. **72**

3 Write the number that is the same as:
a. three tens and six ones (units) **36**
b. eight tens and three ones (units) **83**
c. five tens and four ones (units) **54**
d. nine tens and no ones (units) **90**

4 Write what the 6 is worth in these numbers.
a. 26 **6 ones (units)** b. 62 **6 tens** c. 60 **6 tens**

5 What would you do to change:
a. 7 into 67? **Add 60** b. 53 into 3? **Subtract 50**

6 Write how many tens and ones (units) there are in these numbers.
a. 47 = **4** tens and **7** ones b. 83 = **8** tens and **3** ones

Name: _____ Date: _____

1 Write these numbers as figures.

a.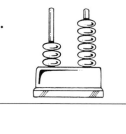

b.

c.

2 Draw these numbers on the abacuses.

a.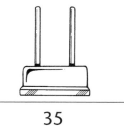

35

b.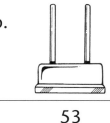

53

c.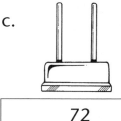

72

3 Write the number that is the same as:

a. three tens and six ones (units)

b. eight tens and three ones (units)

c. five tens and four ones (units)

d. nine tens and no ones (units)

4 Write what the 6 is worth in these numbers.

a. 26

b. 62

c. 60

5 What would you do to change:

a. 7 into 67?

b. 53 into 3?

6 Write how many tens and ones (units) there are in these numbers.

a. 47 = ☐ tens and ☐ ones   b. 83 = ☐ tens and ☐ ones

Place value and ordering

Activity sheet questions

- Read and write whole numbers to at least 100 in figures and words.
- Know what each digit in a two-digit number represents, including 0 as a place holder, and partition two-digit numbers into a multiple of ten and ones (TU). Use the = sign to represent equality.

Oral 1–10 & Written 1–2
- **Use and begin to read the vocabulary of comparing and ordering numbers, including ordinal numbers to 100.**

3–5
- **Compare two given two-digit numbers, say which is more or less, and give a number which lies between them.**
- Say the number that is 1 or 10 more or less than any given two-digit number.
- Order whole numbers to at least 100, and position them on a number line and 100 square.

Teacher note

- A wide range of vocabulary of comparing and ordering should be developed, including ordinal numbers (first, second, third etc.).

Oral questions

Which is more:
1. 17 or 31?
2. 54 or 45?
3. 67 or 76?

Which is longer:
4. 37cm or 29cm?
5. 80m or 69m?

Which is less:
6. 73 or 37?
7. 31 or 28?
8. 87 or 90?

Which is shorter:
9. 16m or 21m?
10. 56cm or 65cm?

Answers

1.	**31**	6.	**37**
2.	**54**	7.	**28**
3.	**76**	8.	**87**
4.	**37cm**	9.	**16m**
5.	**80m**	10.	**56cm**

1 What position is the white square?

Eighth

2 What position is the third white square?

Seventh

3 Clare has 17 pens. Mia has 25 pens. Who has fewer pens?

Clare

4 Alice has 36 sweets. Emily has 39 sweets and Omar has 28 sweets.

a. Who has most sweets? **Emily**

b. How many more sweets does Alice have than Omar? **8**

c. How many fewer sweets does Omar have than Emily? **11**

5 Write an odd number that lies between:

a. 16 and 20 **17 or 19** b. 49 and 53 **51** c. 95 and 100 **97 or 99**

Name: _____   Date: _____

ASSESSMENT 7 — Place value and ordering

1.	6.
2.	7.
3.	8.
4.	9.
5.	10.

1 What position is the white square?

2 What position is the third white square?

3 Clare has 17 pens. Mia has 25 pens.
Who has fewer pens?

4 Alice has 36 sweets. Emily has 39 sweets and Omar has 28 sweets.

a. Who has most sweets?

b. How many more sweets does Alice have than Omar?

c. How many fewer sweets does Omar have than Emily?

5 Write an odd number that lies between:

a. 16 and 20   b. 49 and 53   c. 95 and 100

Place value and ordering

Activity sheet questions

- Read and write whole numbers to at least 100 in figures and words.
- Know what each digit in a two-digit number represents, including 0 as a place holder, and partition two-digit numbers into a multiple of ten and ones (TU).
- Use and begin to read the vocabulary of comparing and ordering numbers, including ordinal numbers to 100.
  Use the = sign to represent equality.
  Compare two given two-digit numbers, say which is more or less, and give a number which lies between them.

Written 1–6
- **Say the number that is 1 or 10 more or less than any given two-digit number.**
- Order whole numbers to at least 100, and position them on a number line and 100 square.

Teacher note

- An understanding of place value is necessary for children to know what is 10 more than or less than a number. Provide place value cards to enable children to see that the ones or units digit remains unchanged. Similarly, the use of 10 and 1 pence coins can enable children to see that the number of 1 pence coins is unaffected by the addition or removal of 10 pence coins.

Answers

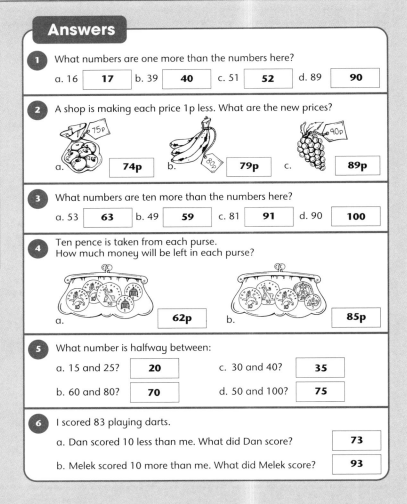

1 What numbers are one more than the numbers here?
a. 16 **17** b. 39 **40** c. 51 **52** d. 89 **90**

2 A shop is making each price 1p less. What are the new prices?
a. **74p** b. **79p** c. **89p**

3 What numbers are ten more than the numbers here?
a. 53 **63** b. 49 **59** c. 81 **91** d. 90 **100**

4 Ten pence is taken from each purse. How much money will be left in each purse?
a. **62p** b. **85p**

5 What number is halfway between:
a. 15 and 25? **20** c. 30 and 40? **35**
b. 60 and 80? **70** d. 50 and 100? **75**

6 I scored 83 playing darts.
a. Dan scored 10 less than me. What did Dan score? **73**
b. Melek scored 10 more than me. What did Melek score? **93**

Place value and ordering

1 What numbers are one more than the numbers here?

a. 16 [ ]   b. 39 [ ]   c. 51 [ ]   d. 89 [ ]

2 A shop is making each price 1p less. What are the new prices?

a. 75p [ ]   b. 80p [ ]   c. 90p [ ]

3 What numbers are ten more than the numbers here?

a. 53 [ ]   b. 49 [ ]   c. 81 [ ]   d. 90 [ ]

4 Ten pence is taken from each purse.
How much money will be left in each purse?

a. [ ]   b. [ ]

5 What number is halfway between:

a. 15 and 25? [ ]   c. 30 and 40? [ ]

b. 60 and 80? [ ]   d. 50 and 100? [ ]

6 I scored 83 playing darts.

a. Dan scored 10 less than me. What did Dan score? [ ]

b. Melek scored 10 more than me. What did Melek score? [ ]

Place value and ordering

Activity sheet questions

- Read and write whole numbers to at least 100 in figures and words.
- Know what each digit in a two-digit number represents, including 0 as a place holder, and partition two-digit numbers into a multiple of ten and ones (TU).
- Use and begin to read the vocabulary of comparing and ordering numbers, including ordinal numbers to 100.
  Use the = sign to represent equality.
  Compare two given two-digit numbers, say which is more or less, and give a number which lies between them.
- Say the number that is 1 or 10 more or less than any given two-digit number.

Written
1–5   ● **Order whole numbers to at least 100, and position them on a number line and 100 square.**

Teacher note

- The use of number lines is essential for comparing and ordering. Counting sticks can be used for further illustration.

Answers

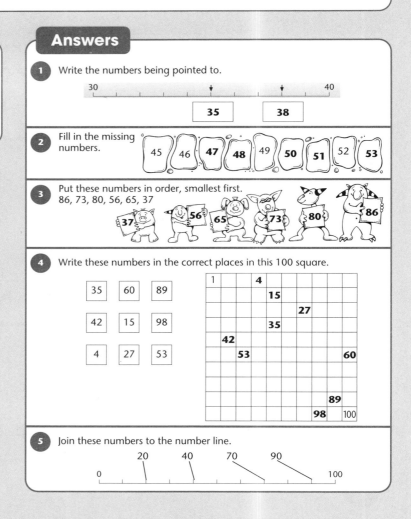

1   Write the numbers being pointed to.

30   ↓   ↓   40

35   38

2   Fill in the missing numbers.
45   46   **47**   48   49   **50**   51   52   53

3   Put these numbers in order, smallest first.
86, 73, 80, 56, 65, 37

37   56   65   73   80   86

4   Write these numbers in the correct places in this 100 square.

35   60   89

42   15   98

4   27   53

1			**4**						
				15					
						27			
				35					
	42								
		53							**60**
								89	
								98	100

5   Join these numbers to the number line.
20   40   70   90

0   100

Name: _____ Date: _____

Place value and ordering

1 Write the numbers being pointed to.

30 ———————↓——————↓———————— 40

[ ]   [ ]

2 Fill in the missing numbers.

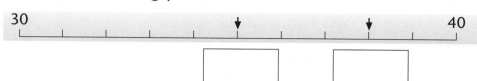

45 46 [ ] [ ] 49 [ ] [ ] 52 [ ]

3 Put these numbers in order, smallest first.
86, 73, 80, 56, 65, 37

4 Write these numbers in the correct places in this 100 square.

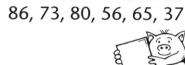

35	60	89
42	15	98
4	27	53

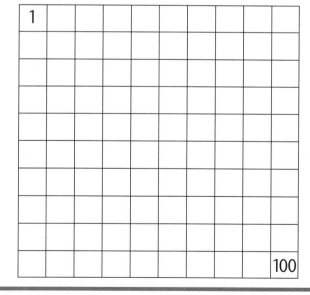

1 ...
... 100

5 Join these numbers to the number line.

20   40   70   90

0 —————————————————————— 100

Estimating and rounding

Activity sheet questions

Written

1–3 • Use and begin to read the vocabulary of estimation and approximation; give a sensible estimate of at least 50 objects.

4 • Round numbers less than 100 to the nearest 10.

Teacher note

• Children sometimes find estimating difficult as they do not like to give an answer that is not necessarily correct. Discuss the usefulness of estimating with children and encourage them to develop simple ways of making estimates more accurate, e.g. getting a rough idea of how many objects are in a quarter or half of a jar, or using things they already know, e.g. I know there are 10 in this jar so there must be more in that jar.

Answers

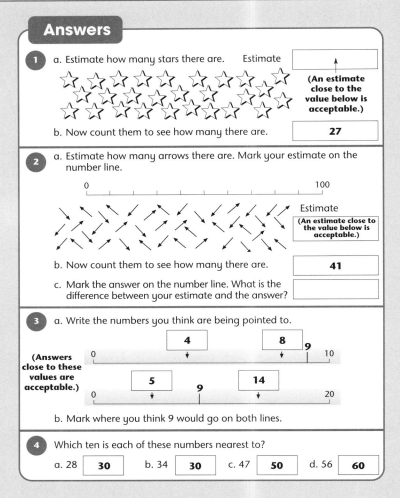

1 a. Estimate how many stars there are. Estimate [ ] (An estimate close to the value below is acceptable.)

b. Now count them to see how many there are. **27**

2 a. Estimate how many arrows there are. Mark your estimate on the number line.

0   100

Estimate (An estimate close to the value below is acceptable.)

b. Now count them to see how many there are. **41**

c. Mark the answer on the number line. What is the difference between your estimate and the answer? [ ]

3 a. Write the numbers you think are being pointed to.

(Answers close to these values are acceptable.)

0   **4**   **8** 9   10

0   **5**   9   **14**   20

b. Mark where you think 9 would go on both lines.

4 Which ten is each of these numbers nearest to?

a. 28 **30**   b. 34 **30**   c. 47 **50**   d. 56 **60**

Name: _____ Date: _____

1 a. Estimate how many stars there are.   Estimate [   ]

b. Now count them to see how many there are.   [   ]

2 a. Estimate how many arrows there are. Mark your estimate on the number line.

0 |___|___|___|___|___|___|___|___|___| 100

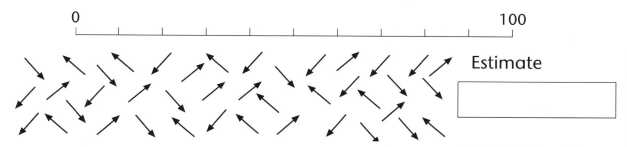

Estimate [   ]

b. Now count them to see how many there are.   [   ]

c. Mark the answer on the number line. What is the difference between your estimate and the answer?   [   ]

3 a. Write the numbers you think are being pointed to.

[   ]   [   ]

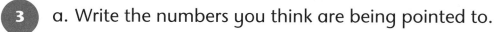
0   ↓   ↓   10

[   ]   [   ]

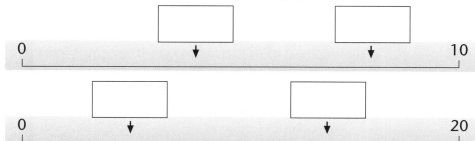
0   ↓   ↓   20

b. Mark where you think 9 would go on both lines.

4 Which ten is each of these numbers nearest to?

a. 28 [   ]   b. 34 [   ]   c. 47 [   ]   d. 56 [   ]

Activity sheet questions

Written

1-7 ● **Begin to recognise and find one half and one quarter of shapes and small numbers of objects.**

Begin to recognise that two halves or four quarters make one whole and that two quarters and one half are equivalent.

Teacher note

● The notation we use to show fractions (e.g. $\frac{1}{4}$) has a denominator that shows how many equal parts something has been divided up into, and a numerator that tells us how many of those parts we have. The use of two numbers, such as 1 and 4, to denote a number less than 1 can be very confusing, since children's experience of ones and fours has been as whole numbers. The idea of a fraction as part of a set of objects is a more complex idea than that of being part of one whole. If we have 12 objects then $\frac{1}{4}$ of them is 3. The notion that 3 can be $\frac{1}{4}$ is confusing for many children and it is essential that they have a good understanding of the meaning of notation such as $\frac{1}{4}$.

Answers

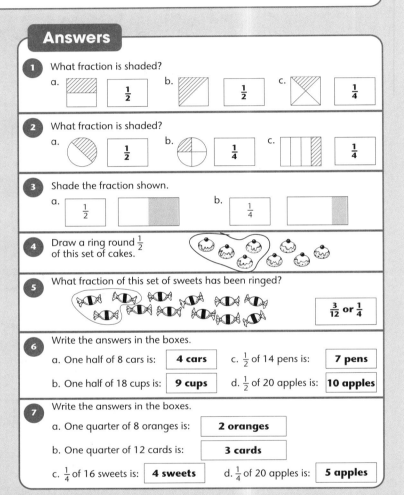

Name: _____ Date: _____

1 What fraction is shaded?

a.    b.   c.

2 What fraction is shaded?

a.   b.   c.

3 Shade the fraction shown.

a. $\frac{1}{2}$    b. $\frac{1}{4}$

4 Draw a ring round $\frac{1}{2}$ of this set of cakes.

5 What fraction of this set of sweets has been ringed?

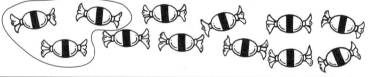

6 Write the answers in the boxes.

a. One half of 8 cars is: [ ]   c. $\frac{1}{2}$ of 14 pens is: [ ]

b. One half of 18 cups is: [ ]   d. $\frac{1}{2}$ of 20 apples is: [ ]

7 Write the answers in the boxes.

a. One quarter of 8 oranges is: [ ]

b. One quarter of 12 cards is: [ ]

c. $\frac{1}{4}$ of 16 sweets is: [ ]   d. $\frac{1}{4}$ of 20 apples is: [ ]

Fractions

Activity sheet questions

Written

1–3 • Begin to recognise and find one half and one quarter of shapes and small numbers of objects.

4–6 Begin to recognise that two halves or four quarters make one whole and that two quarters and one half are equivalent.

Teacher note

• Children often have more difficulty in describing fractions of sets, as in 'ring a quarter of the sweets' than with fractions of areas, e.g. 'shade a quarter of the cake'. It is more difficult to visualise 4 sweets as a whole than 1 cake or 1 square, etc.

Answers

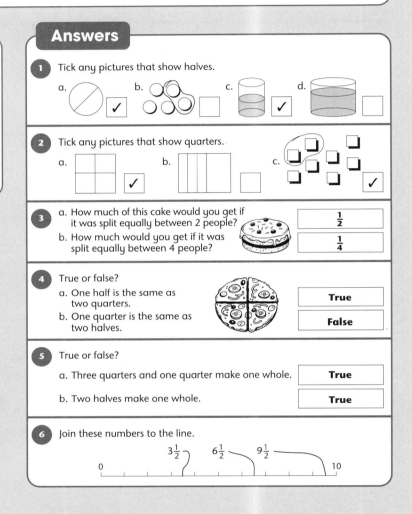

1. Tick any pictures that show halves.

   a. ✓   b. ☐   c. ✓   d. ☐

2. Tick any pictures that show quarters.

   a. ✓   b. ☐   c. ✓

3. a. How much of this cake would you get if it was split equally between 2 people? $\frac{1}{2}$
   b. How much would you get if it was split equally between 4 people? $\frac{1}{4}$

4. True or false?
   a. One half is the same as two quarters.   **True**
   b. One quarter is the same as two halves.   **False**

5. True or false?
   a. Three quarters and one quarter make one whole.   **True**
   b. Two halves make one whole.   **True**

6. Join these numbers to the line.

   $3\frac{1}{2}$ $6\frac{1}{2}$ $9\frac{1}{2}$

   0 ————————————————— 10

Name: _____   Date: _____

1 Tick any pictures that show halves.

a. ⊘ ☐   b.  ☐   c.   d. 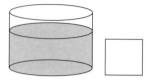 ☐

2 Tick any pictures that show quarters.

a.    b. 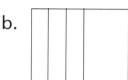   c.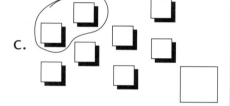

3 a. How much of this cake would you get if it was split equally between 2 people?

    b. How much would you get if it was split equally between 4 people?

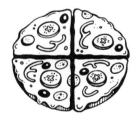

☐

☐

4 True or false?

    a. One half is the same as two quarters.

    b. One quarter is the same as two halves.

☐

☐

5 True or false?

    a. Three quarters and one quarter make one whole.

    b. Two halves make one whole.

☐

☐

6 Join these numbers to the line.

$$3\frac{1}{2} \qquad 6\frac{1}{2} \qquad 9\frac{1}{2}$$

0 ├─┼─┼─┼─┼─┼─┼─┼─┼─┼─┤ 10

Understanding addition

Activity sheet questions

Oral
1–10
- Extend understanding of the operation of addition.
  Use and begin to read the related vocabulary.

Written
1–3
Use the +, – and = signs to record mental additions and subtractions in a number sentence, and recognise the use of a symbol such as ☐ or ◯ to stand for an unknown number.
Recognise that addition can be done in any order, but not subtraction: for example, 3 + 21 = 21 + 3, but 21 – 3 ≠ 3 – 21.
- Understand that more than two numbers can be added.
  Begin to add three single-digit numbers mentally (totals up to about 20) or three two-digit numbers with the help of apparatus (totals up to 100).
- Understand that subtraction is the inverse of addition (subtraction reverses addition).

Teacher note

- Children need to have experience of a wide range of addition vocabulary, e.g. 'plus', 'add', 'and', 'altogether', 'sum', 'total'.

Oral questions

1. 15 add 10.
2. 13 plus 4.
3. 16 and 6 more.
4. Add 12 to 20.
5. What is the sum of 18 and 7?
6. What is the total of 4 and 23?
7. What must I add to 14 to make 18?
8. How many are 16 and 4 altogether?
9. I am thinking of a number. I add 10. The answer is 25. What is my number?
10. 5 plus 3 plus 12 equals how many?

Answers

1.	**25**	6.	**27**
2.	**17**	7.	**4**
3.	**22**	8.	**20**
4.	**32**	9.	**15**
5.	**25**	10.	**20**

1 Fill in the missing numbers.

a. 3 + 6 = **9**   c. 4 + △**5** = 9   e. (**8**) + 2 = 10

b. 12 + 4 = **16**   d. 30 + △**7** = 37   f. (**12**) + 24 = 36

2 Only one of these number sentences is true. Tick the one that is true.

14 + 5 = 20   14 – 5 = 5 – 14

✓ 14 + 5 = 5 + 14   19 = 13 + 5

3 Use this number line to help you answer the following questions.

0 1 2 3 4 5 6 7 8 9 10 11 12 13 14 15 16 17 18 19 20

a. 3 + 6 + 5 = (**14**)   c. 5 + 9 + 6 = (**20**)   e. 2 + 7 + 3 = (**12**)

b. 1 + 8 + 7 = (**16**)   d. 12 + 2 + 6 = (**20**)   f. 3 + 8 + 9 = (**20**)

Name: _____   Date: _____

1.	6.
2.	7.
3.	8.
4.	9.
5.	10.

1 Fill in the missing numbers.

a. $3 + 6 =$ ▢

b. $12 + 4 =$ ▢

c. $4 + \triangle = 9$

d. $30 + \triangle = 37$

e. $\bigcirc + 2 = 10$

f. $\bigcirc + 24 = 36$

2 Only one of these number sentences is true. Tick the one that is true.

| 14 | + | 5 | = | 20 | | 14 | − | 5 | = | 5 | − | 14 |

| 14 | + | 5 | = | 5 | + | 14 | | 19 | = | 13 | + | 5 |

3 Use this number line to help you answer the following questions.

0 1 2 3 4 5 6 7 8 9 10 11 12 13 14 15 16 17 18 19 20

a. $3 + 6 + 5 =$ ◯

b. $1 + 8 + 7 =$ ◯

c. $5 + 9 + 6 =$ ◯

d. $12 + 2 + 6 =$ ◯

e. $2 + 7 + 3 =$ ◯

f. $3 + 8 + 9 =$ ◯

Understanding subtraction

Activity sheet questions

Oral
1–10
- Extend understanding of the operation of subtraction.
  Use and begin to read the related vocabulary.

Written
1–3
  Use the +, – and = signs to record mental additions and subtractions in a number sentence, and recognise the use of a symbol such as ☐ or ◯ to stand for an unknown number.
  Recognise that addition can be done in any order, but not subtraction: for example, 3 + 21 = 21 + 3, but 21 – 3 ≠ 3 – 21.
- Understand that more than two numbers can be added.
  Begin to add three single-digit numbers mentally (totals up to about 20) or three two-digit numbers with the help of apparatus (totals up to 100).
- Understand that subtraction is the inverse of addition (subtraction reverses addition).

Teacher note

- Children need to have experience of a wide range of subtraction vocabulary, e.g. 'take away', 'subtract', 'difference between', 'less than', 'how many are left'.

Oral questions

1. 8 take away 2.
2. 7 subtract 3.
3. Take 3 from 14.
4. 5 less than 16.
5. How many less than 20 is 5?
6. Subtract 7 from 19.
7. What is the difference between 5 and 15?
8. How many more than 12 is 19?
9. Write two numbers that have a difference of 13.
10. I am thinking of a number. I subtract 10. The answer is 12. What is my number?

Answers

1. **6**	6. **12**
2. **4**	7. **10**
3. **11**	8. **7**
4. **11**	9. **(Two numbers that have a difference of 13.)**
5. **15**	10. **22**

1 Fill in the missing numbers.

a. 7 – 1 = **6**   c. 9 – △**4** = 5   e. ⬭**7** – 4 = 3

b. 16 – 3 = **13**   d. 24 – △**10** = 14   f. ⬭**45** – 15 = 30

2 Use this number line to help you answer these questions.

0 1 2 3 4 5 6 7 8 9 10 11 12 13 14 15 16 17 18 19 20

a. 15 – 8 = **7**   c. 16 – 12 = **4**   e. 17 – 8 = **9**

b. 18 – 7 = **11**   d. 20 – 6 = **14**   f. 19 – 4 = **15**

3 Write two numbers with a difference of: **(Children's answers will vary.)**

a. 7 ☐   c. 12 ☐   e. 14 ☐

b. 16 ☐   d. 18 ☐   f. 20 ☐

Name: _____   Date: _____

ASSESSMENT 14

Understanding subtraction

1.	6.
2.	7.
3.	8.
4.	9.
5.	10.

1 Fill in the missing numbers.

a. $7 - 1 = \boxed{}$

b. $16 - 3 = \boxed{}$

c. $9 - \triangle = 5$

d. $24 - \triangle = 14$

e. $\bigcirc - 4 = 3$

f. $\bigcirc - 15 = 30$

2 Use this number line to help you answer these questions.

0 1 2 3 4 5 6 7 8 9 10 11 12 13 14 15 16 17 18 19 20

a. $15 - 8 = \bigcirc$

b. $18 - 7 = \bigcirc$

c. $16 - 12 = \bigcirc$

d. $20 - 6 = \bigcirc$

e. $17 - 8 = \bigcirc$

f. $19 - 4 = \bigcirc$

3 Write two numbers with a difference of:

a. $\boxed{7}$ $\boxed{}$

b. $\boxed{16}$ $\boxed{}$

c. $\boxed{12}$ $\boxed{}$

d. $\boxed{18}$ $\boxed{}$

e. $\boxed{14}$ $\boxed{}$

f. $\boxed{20}$ $\boxed{}$

Activity sheet questions

Oral
1–10
& Written
1–2
3–5

- **Use knowledge that addition can be done in any order to do mental calculations more efficiently. For example:**
  - **put the larger number first and count on in tens or ones**
  - **add three small numbers by putting the largest number first and/or find a pair totalling 10**
  - partition into '5 and a bit' when adding 6, 7, 8 or 9, then recombine (e.g. 16 + 8 = 15 + 1 + 5 + 3 = 20 + 4 = 24)
  - partition additions into tens and units, then recombine.
- Find a small difference by counting up from the smaller to the larger number (e.g. 42 – 39).
- Identify near doubles, using doubles already known (e.g. 8 + 9, 40 + 41).
- Add/subtract 9 or 11: add/subtract 10 and adjust by 1.
  Begin to add/subtract 19 or 21: add/subtract 20 and adjust by 1.
- Use patterns of similar calculations.
- State the subtraction corresponding to a given addition, and vice versa.
- Use known number facts and place value to add/subtract mentally.
- Bridge through 10 or 20, then adjust.

Teacher note

- Help children to develop a range of strategies, e.g. when adding 11, add 10 and add a further 1, etc. Remind children that the order does not matter when adding.

Oral questions

1. 23 add 6.
2. 24 and 5.
3. 10 plus 43.
4. 20 and 27 make how many altogether?
5. What is the total of 20 and 6?
6. 30 and 22?
7. 7 plus 38.
8. 40 add 27.
9. Add 17 and 6.
10. 19 plus 8.

Answers

1.	**29**	6.	**52**
2.	**29**	7.	**45**
3.	**53**	8.	**67**
4.	**47**	9.	**23**
5.	**26**	10.	**27**

1 Write the answers in the boxes.

a. 5 + 24 = **29**

b. 4 + 57 = **61**

c. 9 + 61 = **70**

2 Write the answers in the boxes.

a. 20 + 40 = **60**

b. 30 + 50 = **80**

c. 20 + 70 = **90**

3 Add these numbers.

a. 8 + 2 + 3 = **13**

b. 4 + 5 + 6 = **15**

4 Now add these numbers.

a. 2 + 9 + 8 = **19**

b. 6 + 8 + 3 = **17**

5 Write the missing numbers in the boxes.

7 + **4** + 6 = 17   b. **10** + 7 + 4 = 21

15   Mental calculation strategies (+ and –)

1.	6.
2.	7.
3.	8.
4.	9.
5.	10.

1   Write the answers in the boxes.

a. $5 + 24 =$

b. $4 + 57 =$

c. $9 + 61 =$

2   Write the answers in the boxes.

a. $20 + 40 =$

b. $30 + 50 =$

c. $20 + 70 =$

3   Add these numbers.

a. $8 + 2 + 3 =$

b. $4 + 5 + 6 =$

4   Now add these numbers.

a. $2 + 9 + 8 =$

b. $6 + 8 + 3 =$

5   Write the missing numbers in the boxes.

$7 +$ ⬚ $+ 6 = 17$ b. ⬚ $+ 7 + 4 = 21$

Activity sheet questions

- Use knowledge that addition can be done in any order to do mental calculations more efficiently. For example:
  - add three small numbers by putting the largest number first and/or find a pair totalling 10

Written

1–2
- put the larger number first and count on in tens or ones

3
- partition into '5 and a bit' when adding 6, 7, 8 or 9, then recombine (e.g. 16 + 8 = 15 + 1 + 5 + 3 = 20 + 4 = 24)

4
- partition additions into tens and units, then recombine.

5
- **Find a small difference by counting up from the smaller to the larger number (e.g. 42 − 39).**

6
- **Identify near doubles, using doubles already known (e.g. 8 + 9, 40 + 41).**
- Add/subtract 9 or 11: add/subtract 10 and adjust by 1. Begin to add/subtract 19 or 21: add/subtract 20 and adjust by 1.
- Use patterns of similar calculations.
- State the subtraction corresponding to a given addition, and vice versa.
- Use known number facts and place value to add/subtract mentally.
- Bridge through 10 or 20, then adjust.

Teacher note

- The use of empty number lines to demonstrate small differences is useful, e.g. from 96 to 101, with arcs to indicate the jump from 96 to 100 and then on to 101.

i.e.

Answers

Put the larger number first to help you add these numbers.

1
a. 5 + 13 = **18**
b. 12 + 17 = **29**

2
a. 9 + 25 = **34**
b. 7 + 24 = **31**

3 Fill in the missing numbers. Add by splitting the numbers into 5 and a bit.

a. 12 = 5 + **7**   c. 18 = 5 + **13**   e. 15 + 7 = **22**

b. 17 = 5 + **12**   d. 15 + 4 = **19**   f. 15 + 9 = **24**

4 Add by splitting the numbers into tens and units.

a. 13 + 24 = **10 + 20 = 30, 3 + 4 = 7, 30 + 7 = 37**

b. 17 + 18 = **10 + 10 = 20, 7 + 8 = 15, 20 + 15 = 35**

5 Do these by counting up.

a. 43 − 39 = **4**   c. 64 − 59 = **5**

b. 52 − 48 = **4**   d. 82 − 78 = **4**

6
a. 7 + 8 = **15**   d. 33 + 32 = **65**

b. 12 + 11 = **23**   e. 40 + 39 = **79**

c. 24 + 25 = **49**   f. 51 + 52 = **103**

Name: _____ Date: _____

Mental calculation strategies (+ and –)

Put the larger number first to help you add these numbers.

1 a. 5 + 13 = [____]

b. 12 + 17= [____]

2 a. 9 + 25 = [____]

b. 7 + 24 = [____]

3 Fill in the missing numbers. Add by splitting the numbers into 5 and a bit.

a. 12 = 5 + △   c. 18 = 5 + △   e. 15 + 7 = [__]

b. 17 = 5 + △   d. 15 + 4 = [__]   f. 15 + 9 = [__]

4 Add by splitting the numbers into tens and units.

a. 13 + 24 = [_____]

b. 17 + 18 = [_____]

5 Do these by counting up.

a. 43 – 39 = [_____]   c. 64 – 59 = [_____]

b. 52 – 48 = [_____]   d. 82 – 78 = [_____]

6 a. 7 + 8 = [_____]   d. 33 + 32 = [_____]

b. 12 + 11 = [_____]   e. 40 + 39 = [_____]

c. 24 + 25 = [_____]   f. 51 + 52 = [_____]

Activity sheet questions

● Use knowledge that addition can be done in any order to do mental calculations more efficiently. For example:
   – put the larger number first and count on in tens or ones
   – add three small numbers by putting the largest number first and/or find a pair totalling 10
   – partition into '5 and a bit' when adding 6, 7, 8 or 9, then recombine (e.g. 16 + 8 = 15 + 1 + 5 + 3 = 20 + 4 = 24)
   – partition additions into tens and units, then recombine.
● Find a small difference by counting up from the smaller to the larger number (e.g. 42 – 39).
● Identify near doubles, using doubles already known (e.g. 8 + 9, 40 + 41).

Written
1–4 ● **Add/subtract 9 or 11: add/subtract 10 and adjust by 1.**
5–6 **Begin to add/subtract 19 or 21: add/subtract 20 and adjust by 1.**
7 ● **Use patterns of similar calculations.**
● State the subtraction corresponding to a given addition, and vice versa.
● Use known number facts and place value to add/subtract mentally.
● Bridge through 10 or 20, then adjust.

Teacher note

● Children should be encouraged to use a wide range of mental calculation strategies and to verbalise the method chosen for each calculation. They should also have experience of recording such calculation strategies using informal jottings.

Answers

1 a. 16 + 11 = **27**   b. 35 + 11 = **46**

2 a. 23 – 11 = **12**   b. 50 – 11 = **39**

3 a. 24 + 9 = **33**   b. 32 + 9 = **41**

4 a. 33 – 9 = **24**   b. 48 – 9 = **39**

5 a. 36 + 21 = **57**   b. 43 + 19 = **62**

6 a. 38 – 21 = **17**   b. 57 – 19 = **38**

7 Continue these patterns.

a.				b.			
5 + 3	=	8		6 – 4	=	2	
5 + 13	=	18		16 – 4	=	12	
5 + 23	=	28		26 – 4	=	22	
5 + **33**	=	**38**		**36** – **4**	=	**32**	
5 + **43**	=	**48**		**46** – **4**	=	**42**	
5 + **53**	=	**58**		**56** – **4**	=	**52**	
5 + **63**	=	**68**		**66** – **4**	=	**62**	

Mental calculation strategies (+ and –)

1   a. 16 + 11 = [   ]   b. 35 + 11 = [   ]

2   a. 23 – 11 = [   ]   b. 50 – 11 = [   ]

3   a. 24 + 9 = [   ]   b. 32 + 9 = [   ]

4   a. 33 – 9 = [   ]   b. 48 – 9 = [   ]

5   a. 36 + 21 = [   ]   b. 43 + 19 = [   ]

6   a. 38 – 21 = [   ]   b. 57 – 19 = [   ]

7   Continue these patterns.

a. 5 + 3 = 8   b. 6 – 4 = 2

   5 + 13 = 18   16 – 4 = 12

   5 + 23 = 28   26 – 4 = 22

   [ ] + [ ] = [ ]   [ ] – [ ] = [ ]

   [ ] + [ ] = [ ]   [ ] – [ ] = [ ]

   [ ] + [ ] = [ ]   [ ] – [ ] = [ ]

   [ ] + [ ] = [ ]   [ ] – [ ] = [ ]

Mental calculation strategies (+ and –)

Activity sheet questions

- Use knowledge that addition can be done in any order to do mental calculations more efficiently. For example:
  - put the larger number first and count on in tens or ones
  - add three small numbers by putting the largest number first and/or find a pair totalling 10
  - partition into '5 and a bit' when adding 6, 7, 8 or 9, then recombine (e.g. 16 + 8 = 15 + 1 + 5 + 3 = 20 + 4 = 24)
  - partition additions into tens and units, then recombine.
- Find a small difference by counting up from the smaller to the larger number (e.g. 42 – 39).
- Identify near doubles, using doubles already known (e.g. 8 + 9, 40 + 41).
- Add/subtract 9 or 11: add/subtract 10 and adjust by 1.
  Begin to add/subtract 19 or 21: add/subtract 20 and adjust by 1.
- Use patterns of similar calculations.

Written

1–3 ● **State the subtraction corresponding to a given addition, and vice versa.**

4–7 ● **Use known number facts and place value to add/subtract mentally.**

8 ● **Bridge through 10 or 20, then adjust.**

Teacher note

- Children should be encouraged to use a wide range of mental calculation strategies and to verbalise the method chosen for each calculation. They should also have experience of recording such calculation strategies using informal jottings.

Answers

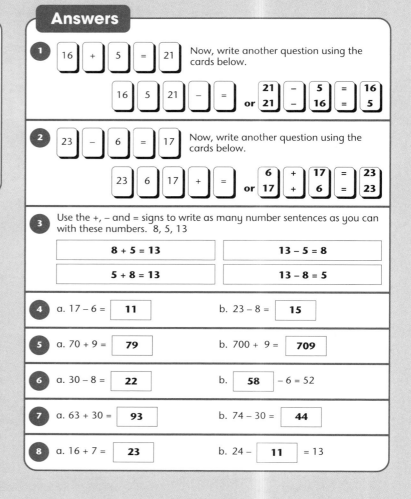

Name: _____ Date: _____

 1 | 16 | + | 5 | = | 21 | Now, write another question using the cards below.

| 16 | 5 | 21 | – | = | | | | | |

2 | 23 | – | 6 | = | 17 | Now, write another question using the cards below.

| 23 | 6 | 17 | + | = | | | | | |

3 Use the +, – and = signs to write as many number sentences as you can with these numbers. 8, 5, 13

4 a. 17 – 6 = [ ]   b. 23 – 8 = [ ]

5 a. 70 + 9 = [ ]   b. 700 + 9 = [ ]

6 a. 30 – 8 = [ ]   b. [ ] – 6 = 52

7 a. 63 + 30 = [ ]   b. 74 – 30 = [ ]

8 a. 16 + 7 = [ ]   b. 24 – [ ] = 13

Activity sheet questions

Oral	
1–10	Use and begin to read the related vocabulary.
Written	
1–2	• Understand the operation of multiplication as repeated addition or as describing an array.
3–4	• Know and use halving as the inverse of doubling.
5	Use the x and = signs to record mental calculations in a number sentence, and recognise the use of a symbol such as ☐ or △ to stand for an unknown number.

Teacher note

• Note the commutative law as it applies to multiplication, i.e. 5 x 3 and 3 x 5 give the same answer.

Oral questions

1. 2 times 5.
2. 3 twos are how many?
3. 5 multiplied by 5.
4. 5 tens are how many?
5. Multiply 4 by 2.
6. How many times bigger than 5 is 15?
7. 6 times 2.
8. Double 5.
9. Is 10 a multiple of 2?
10. Is 24 a multiple of 5?

Answers

1.	**10**	6.	**3**
2.	**6**	7.	**12**
3.	**25**	8.	**10**
4.	**50**	9.	**Yes**
5.	**8**	10.	**No**

1 True or false?

a. 5 x 3 is the same as 5 + 5 + 5 — **True**

b. 5 + 4 = 4 x 4 x 4 x 4 x 4 — **False**

2 What does this picture show? Write the missing numbers in the boxes.

5 x **2** = **10**

(Or 2 x 5 = 10)

3 a. If 12 x 2 = 24, what is 24 ÷ 2? — **12**

b. If 18 x 2 = 36, what is 36 ÷ 2? — **18**

4 a. Double 23 is 46. Half of 46 is: — **23**

b. Half of 52 is 26. Double 26 is: — **52**

5 Write the missing numbers.

a. 8 x 2 = **16**

b. 2 x 9 = **18**

c. 10 x 2 = **20**

d. 5 x **4** = 20

e. **2** x 4 = 8

f. **4** x 10 = 40

Name: _____ Date: _____

1.	6.
2.	7.
3.	8.
4.	9.
5.	10.

1 True or false? a. 5 x 3 is the same as 5 + 5 + 5 [ ]

b. 5 + 4 = 4 x 4 x 4 x 4 x 4 [ ]

2 What does this picture show? Write the missing numbers in the boxes.

[ ] x [ ] = [ ]

3 a. If 12 x 2 = 24, what is 24 ÷ 2? b. If 18 x 2 = 36, what is 36 ÷ 2?

[ ] [ ]

4 a. Double 23 is 46. Half of 46 is: b. Half of 52 is 26. Double 26 is:

[ ] [ ]

5 Write the missing numbers.

a. 8 x 2 = [ ]   c. 10 x 2 = △   e. △ x 4 = 8

b. 2 x 9 = △   d. 5 x [ ] = 20   f. [ ] x 10 = 40

Understanding division

Activity sheet questions

Oral

1-10   Use and begin to read the related vocabulary.

Written

1-2   Begin to understand division as grouping (repeated subtraction) or sharing.

3-4   Use the ÷ and = signs to record mental calculations in a number sentence, and recognise the use of a symbol such as ☐ or △ to stand for an unknown number.

● Know and use halving as the inverse of doubling.

Teacher note

● Children need plenty of experience of situations that can be modelled as sharing and grouping, for example:

1. sharing – I have 8 sweets to share between 4 children. How many sweets does each child get?

2. grouping – I have 8 sweets and I want to give 2 to each child. How many children get sweets?

Oral questions

1. Share 14 between 2.
2. Share 20 between 2.
3. Divide 20 by 10.
4. How many fives make 20?
5. How many tens make 20?
6. What is half of 16?
7. Halve 20.
8. How many 10p coins do you get for 30p?
9. How many £1 coins do you get for £10?
10. How many £2 coins do you get for £20?

Answers

1. **7**		6. **8**	
2. **10**		7. **10**	
3. **2**		8. **3**	
4. **4**		9. **10**	
5. **2**		10. **10**	

1 This rope is 20cm long.

a. How many 2cm long pieces can we cut from it?   **10**

b. How many 5cm long pieces can we cut from it?   **4**

c. How many 10cm pieces can we cut from it?   **2**

2 Share 12 apples equally between 2 children. How many apples does each child get?   **6**

3 Write two division statements using these numbers. 20, 10, 2

20 ÷ 10 = 2	**20 ÷ 2 = 10**

4 Write the missing numbers.

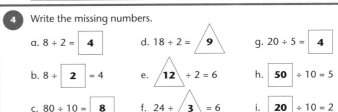

a. 8 ÷ 2 = **4**   d. 18 ÷ 2 = **9**   g. 20 ÷ 5 = **4**

b. 8 ÷ **2** = 4   e. **12** ÷ 2 = 6   h. **50** ÷ 10 = 5

c. 80 ÷ 10 = **8**   f. 24 ÷ **3** = 6   i. **20** ÷ 10 = 2

Name: _____   Date: _____

1.	6.
2.	7.
3.	8.
4.	9.
5.	10.

1 This rope is 20cm long.

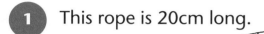

a. How many 2cm long pieces can we cut from it? [ ]

b. How many 5cm long pieces can we cut from it? [ ]

c. How many 10cm pieces can we cut from it? [ ]

2 Share 12 apples equally between 2 children. How many apples does each child get? [ ]

3 Write two division statements using these numbers. 20, 10, 2

[ ]   [ ]

4 Write the missing numbers.

a. $8 \div 2 =$ [ ]

b. $8 \div$ [ ] $= 4$

c. $80 \div 10 =$ [ ]

d. $18 \div 2 = \triangle$

e. $\triangle \div 2 = 6$

f. $24 \div \triangle = 6$

g. $20 \div 5 =$ [ ]

h. [ ] $\div 10 = 5$

i. [ ] $\div 10 = 2$

Reasoning about numbers or shapes

Activity sheet questions

Written

1–5
- **Solve mathematical problems or puzzles, recognise simple patterns and relationships, generalise and predict.**
  Suggest extensions by asking 'What if … ?' or 'What could I try next?'
- Investigate a general statement about familiar numbers or shapes by finding examples that satisfy it.
- Explain how a problem was solved orally and, where appropriate, in writing.

Teacher note

- These questions emphasise the using and applying aspects of mathematics, including simplifying, being systematic, generalising, trial and error, interpreting, etc. These are the abilities that allow children to make use of their mathematics in context. Many children who can successfully multiply, for example, have difficulty when faced with a multiplication question in problem form, often because of an inability to organise their thinking sufficiently. The abilities of simplifying, being systematic, etc. develop through repeated experiences of situations that require these skills.

Answers

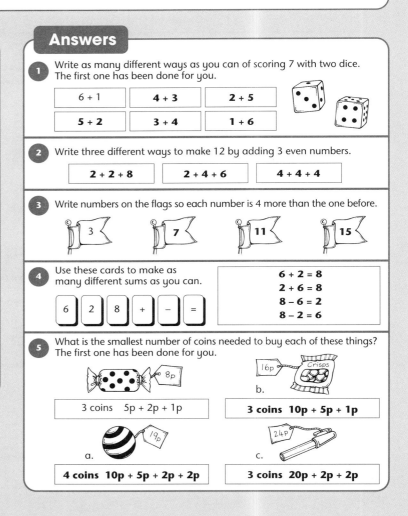

1 Write as many different ways as you can of scoring 7 with two dice. The first one has been done for you.

| 6 + 1 | 4 + 3 | 2 + 5 |
| 5 + 2 | 3 + 4 | 1 + 6 |

2 Write three different ways to make 12 by adding 3 even numbers.

| 2 + 2 + 8 | 2 + 4 + 6 | 4 + 4 + 4 |

3 Write numbers on the flags so each number is 4 more than the one before.

3   7   11   15

4 Use these cards to make as many different sums as you can.

6   2   8   +   −   =

6 + 2 = 8
2 + 6 = 8
8 − 6 = 2
8 − 2 = 6

5 What is the smallest number of coins needed to buy each of these things? The first one has been done for you.

8p

3 coins   5p + 2p + 1p

16p   Crisps
b.

3 coins 10p + 5p + 1p

19p
a.

4 coins 10p + 5p + 2p + 2p

24p
c.

3 coins 20p + 2p + 2p

Name: _____ Date: _____

1 Write as many different ways as you can of scoring 7 with two dice. The first one has been done for you.

6 + 1		

2 Write three different ways to make 12 by adding 3 even numbers.

3 Write numbers on the flags so each number is 4 more than the one before.

4 Use these cards to make as many different sums as you can.

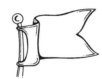 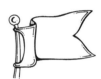

5 What is the smallest number of coins needed to buy each of these things? The first one has been done for you.

b.

3 coins   5p + 2p + 1p

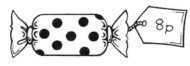

a.

c.

Reasoning about numbers or shapes

Activity sheet questions

● Solve mathematical problems or puzzles, recognise simple patterns and relationships, generalise and predict.
Suggest extensions by asking 'What if … ?' or 'What could I try next?'

Written

1–5 ● **Investigate a general statement about familiar numbers or shapes by finding examples that satisfy it.**

6 ● **Explain how a problem was solved orally and, where appropriate, in writing.**

Teacher note

● Children need to appreciate that more than one example must be given to prove a general statement.

Answers

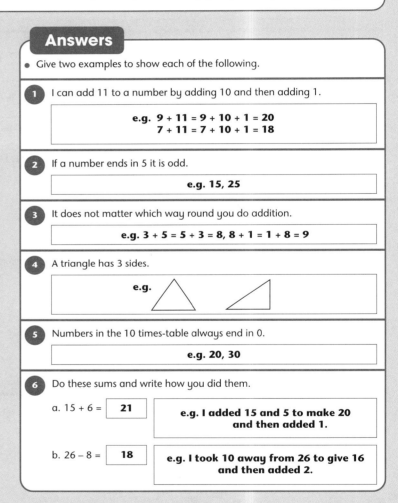

● Give two examples to show each of the following.

1 I can add 11 to a number by adding 10 and then adding 1.

e.g. 9 + 11 = 9 + 10 + 1 = 20
7 + 11 = 7 + 10 + 1 = 18

2 If a number ends in 5 it is odd.

e.g. 15, 25

3 It does not matter which way round you do addition.

e.g. 3 + 5 = 5 + 3 = 8, 8 + 1 = 1 + 8 = 9

4 A triangle has 3 sides.

e.g.

5 Numbers in the 10 times-table always end in 0.

e.g. 20, 30

6 Do these sums and write how you did them.

a. 15 + 6 = 21

e.g. I added 15 and 5 to make 20 and then added 1.

b. 26 − 8 = 18

e.g. I took 10 away from 26 to give 16 and then added 2.

Name: _____ Date: _____

● Give two examples to show each of the following.

1 I can add 11 to a number by adding 10 and then adding 1.

2 If a number ends in 5 it is odd.

3 It does not matter which way round you do addition.

4 A triangle has 3 sides.

5 Numbers in the 10 times-table always end in 0.

6 Do these sums and write how you did them.

a. 15 + 6 = [ ]

b. 26 − 8 = [ ]

Problems involving 'real life' and measures

Activity sheet questions

Oral
1–10
& Written
1–6

● Use mental addition and subtraction, simple multiplication and division, to solve simple word problems involving numbers in 'real life' and measures, using one or two steps.

Teacher note

● Children may initially need to support their mental work with jottings for the 'two-step' problems.

Oral questions

1. I am thinking of a number. If I double it, the answer is 16. What is my number?
2. I am thinking of a number. If I halve it, the answer is 12. What is my number?
3. There are 12 sweets. 4 people share them equally. How many does each person get?
4. 2 girls have 10 crayons each. How many crayons do they have altogether?
5. There are 8 people on a bus. 5 more people get on. How many are on the bus now?
6. An elephant has 4 legs. How many legs do 2 elephants have?
7. There are 6 people on a bus. 7 more get on and 3 get off. How many people are on the bus now?
8. There are 9 apples in a box. Jo puts 4 more in and Deepa puts 7 more in. How many apples are in the box now?
9. There are 10 apples in a box. Jack puts 6 more in and Molly takes 8 out. How many apples are in the box now?
10. If there are 6 eggs in a box, how many eggs are in 10 boxes?

Answers

1. **8**		6. **8**
2. **24**		7. **10**
3. **3**		8. **20**
4. **20**		9. **8**
5. **13**		10. **60**

1 Tom and Katie have 12 toys each.
a. How many toys do they have altogether ? | **24** |

Tom gives 3 toys to Katie.
b. How many does Tom have now? | **9** |

How many does Katie have now? | **15** |

2 There are 5 blue pens and 3 red pens in a packet. How many pens are there in 10 packets? | **80** |

3 Neil left his house for school at 8:00. He arrived at school at 8:30. How long did the journey take? | **30 minutes** |

4 Jennie got off the train at 10:15. The journey took 45 minutes. What time did she get on the train? | **9:30** |

5 Jill's table is 60cm wide. Laura's table is 15cm wider. How wide is Laura's table? | **75cm** |

6 There are 60 litres of water in a tank. How many 10 litre buckets can be filled? | **6** |

Name: _____ Date: _____

1.	6.
2.	7.
3.	8.
4.	9.
5.	10.

1 Tom and Katie have 12 toys each.

a. How many toys do they have altogether ?

Tom gives 3 toys to Katie.

b. How many does Tom have now?

How many does Katie have now?

2 There are 5 blue pens and 3 red pens in a packet. How many pens are there in 10 packets?

3 Neil left his house for school at 8:00. He arrived at school at 8:30. How long did the journey take?

4 Jennie got off the train at 10:15. The journey took 45 minutes. What time did she get on the train?

5 Jill's table is 60cm wide. Laura's table is 15cm wider. How wide is Laura's table?

6 There are 60 litres of water in a tank. How many 10 litre buckets can be filled?

Problems involving money

Activity sheet questions

Oral
1–10
& Written
1–5

- Use mental addition and subtraction, simple multiplication and division, to solve simple word problems involving numbers in money, using one or two steps.
- Recognise all coins and begin to use £.p notation for money (for example, know that £4.65 indicates £4 and 65p). Find totals, give change, and work out which coins to pay.

Teacher note

- Children will need plenty of practice if they are to become confident in working out money problems of these kinds.

Oral questions

1. How many pence is £1.00?
2. How many pence is £2.50?
3. Write 135p in pounds and pence.
4. Write £3.25 in pence.
5. I have £12 and get another £9. How much do I have now?
6. I have 15p and I give 6p to my friend. How much do I have now?
7. A ruler costs 20p more than a pencil. A pencil costs 12p. How much does a ruler cost?
8. A bag of crisps costs 15p more than a chocolate bar. A bag of crisps costs 35p. How much does a chocolate bar cost?
9. Paul bought 3 apples at 12p each. How much did he spend?
10. Sam bought 2 bananas at 20p each. How much change did she get from 50p?

Answers

1.	**100**	6.	**9p**
2.	**250**	7.	**32p**
3.	**£1.35**	8.	**20p**
4.	**325p**	9.	**36p**
5.	**£21**	10.	**10p**

1 How much is this?   **85p**

2 How much is this?   **93p**

3 Write number sentences to show how you do the following.
a. I have 25p and I am given 13p more. How much do I have now?

25p + 13p = 38p

b. Paul spent £18. He spent £9 less than Ali. How much did Ali spend?

£18 + £9 = £27

4 You have four 10p coins, two 5p coins and three 2p coins. How much money do you have?   **56p**

5 Dan has two 20p stamps and two 5p stamps. What different amounts can he make?
20p, 40p, 25p, 30p, 45p, 50p, 5p, 10p

Name: _____ Date: _____

24 | **Problems involving money**

1.	6.
2.	7.
3.	8.
4.	9.
5.	10.

1 How much is this?

2 How much is this?

3 Write number sentences to show how you do the following.

a. I have 25p and I am given 13p more. How much do I have now?

b. Paul spent £18. He spent £9 less than Ali. How much did Ali spend?

4 You have four 10p coins, two 5p coins and three 2p coins. How much money do you have?

5 Dan has two 20p stamps and two 5p stamps. What different amounts can he make?

Activity sheet questions

Written

1–3
- Solve a given problem by sorting, classifying and organising information in simple ways, such as:
  - in a list or simple table
  - in a pictogram
  - in a block graph.

  Discuss and explain results.

Teacher note

- Children may require support in reading and interpreting these questions. Ensure that they understand what is being asked in each one. They should be encouraged to further discuss the tables and charts and explain their observations. Similar contexts and means of representation should be explored in daily mathematics lessons and children should also be involved in the collection of data.

Answers

1

a. Write a list of five different numbers between 50 and 70.

> **(Any five numbers between 50 and 70.)**

b. Write a list of odd numbers from 20 to 40.

> **21, 23, 25, 27, 29, 31, 33, 35, 37, 39**

c. Write a list of five multiples of 2.

> **e.g. 2, 4, 6, 8, 10**

2 Fill in the table to show how many letters these months have.

March April May June July August

3 letters	4 letters	5 letters	6 letters
May	**June July**	**March April**	**August**

3 This chart shows the favourite animals of children in Class 2.

Children in Class 2

a. Which is the favourite animal of most children?

> **Elephant**

b. How many children chose tiger?

> **4**

c. How many more children chose elephant than lion?

> **3**

d. How many children are in Class 2?

> **15**

ASSESSMENT 25

Organising and using data

1

a. Write a list of five different numbers between 50 and 70.

b. Write a list of odd numbers from 20 to 40.

c. Write a list of five multiples of 2.

2 Fill in the table to show how many letters these months have.

March April May June July August

3 letters	4 letters	5 letters	6 letters

3 This chart shows the favourite animals of children in Class 2.

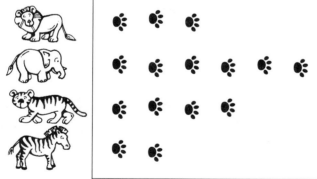

Children in Class 2

a. Which is the favourite animal of most children?

b. How many children chose tiger?

c. How many more children chose elephant than lion?

d. How many children are in Class 2?

Activity sheet questions

Written

1–2
- Solve a given problem by sorting, classifying and organising information in simple ways, such as:
  - in a list or simple table
  - in a block graph
  - in a pictogram.

  Discuss and explain results.

Teacher note

- Children may require support in reading and interpreting the questions. Ensure that they understand what is being asked in each one. They should be encouraged to further discuss the tables and charts and explain their observations. Similar contexts and means of representation should be explored in daily mathematics lessons and children should also be involved in the collection of data.

Answers

1 This graph shows the favourite sports of children in Class 2.

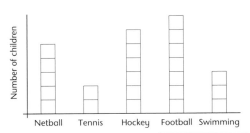

a. Which is the most popular sport? — **Football**

b. Which is the second most popular sport? — **Hockey**

c. How many children chose netball? — **5**

d. How many more children chose football than tennis? — **5**

e. How many children were asked? — **23**

2 Class 2 counted the traffic passing their school. They made a table.

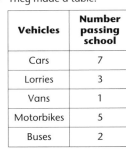

Vehicles	Number passing school
Cars	7
Lorries	3
Vans	1
Motorbikes	5
Buses	2

Draw this on to a graph by colouring in squares.

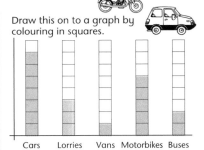

Cars Lorries Vans Motorbikes Buses

Name: _____ Date: _____

1 This graph shows the favourite sports of children in Class 2.

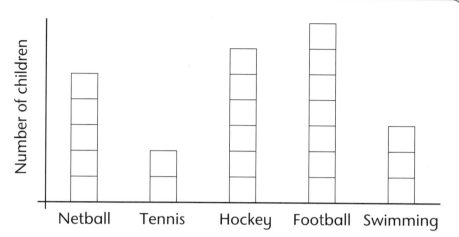

Number of children

Netball   Tennis   Hockey   Football   Swimming

a. Which is the most popular sport?

b. Which is the second most popular sport?

c. How many children chose netball?

d. How many more children chose football than tennis?

e. How many children were asked?

2 Class 2 counted the traffic passing their school. They made a table.

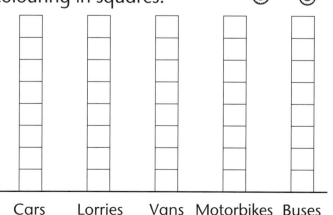

Vehicles	Number passing school
Cars	7
Lorries	3
Vans	1
Motorbikes	5
Buses	2

Draw this on to a graph by colouring in squares.

Cars   Lorries   Vans   Motorbikes   Buses

Activity sheet questions

Oral
1–10
- Use and begin to read the vocabulary related to length, mass and capacity.
- Estimate, measure and compare lengths, masses and capacities, using standard units (m, cm, kg, litre); suggest suitable units and equipment for such measurements.

Written
1–4
- Read a simple scale to the nearest labelled division, including using a ruler to draw and measure lines to the nearest centimetre, recording estimates and measurements as '3 and a bit metres long' or 'about 8 centimetres' or 'nearly 3 kilograms heavy'.
- Use and begin to read the vocabulary related to time.
  Use units of time and know the relationships between them (second, minute, hour, day, week).
  Suggest suitable units to estimate or measure time.
  Order the months of the year.
  Read the time to the hour, half hour or quarter hour on an analogue clock and a 12-hour digital clock, and understand the notation 7:30.

Teacher note

- Children need to have practical experience of these units in order to understand them fully.
- Children will require a ruler for this assessment.

Oral questions

1. How many grams are in a kilogram?
2. True or false – 100cm equals 1m?
3. How many millilitres are in a litre?
4. Write something that is longer than 1m.
5. Write something that is lighter than 1kg.
6. Write something you might measure in centimetres.
7. Write something you might measure in kilograms.
8. What units would you measure the length of the wall in?
9. What units would you use to measure the width of a piece of paper?
10. What units would you use to measure how much a jug holds?

Answers

1.	**1000g**	6.	**e.g. Table width**
2.	**True**	7.	**e.g. My weight**
3.	**1000ml**	8.	**metres**
4.	**e.g. Window**	9.	**centimetres**
5.	**e.g. Pencil**	10.	**millilitres**

1 Estimate the length of these lines. Then measure them.

_____

a. My estimate is [ ] long.   It is **6cm** long.

_____

b. My estimate is [ ] long.   It is **8cm** long.

_____

c. My estimate is [ ] long.   It is **9.5cm** long.

2 How long is the snake?

50cm

3 How much water is in the jug?

375ml

4 How tall is the dog?

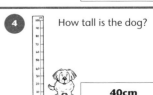

40cm

Name: _____   Date: _____

1.	6.
2.	7.
3.	8.
4.	9.
5.	10.

1 Estimate the length of these lines. Then measure them.

_____

a. My estimate is [   ] long.   It is [   ] long.

_____

b. My estimate is [   ] long.   It is [   ] long.

_____

c. My estimate is [   ] long.   It is [   ] long.

2 How long is the snake?

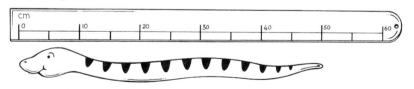

[   ]

3 How much water is in the jug?

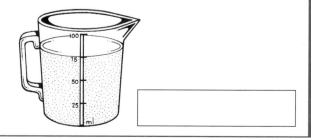

[   ]

4 How tall is the dog?

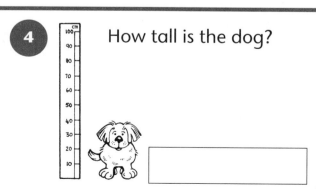

[   ]

Activity sheet questions

- Use and begin to read the vocabulary related to length, mass and capacity.
- Estimate, measure and compare lengths, masses and capacities, using standard units (m, cm, kg, litre); suggest suitable units and equipment for such measurements.

Written 1–4

- **Read a simple scale to the nearest labelled division, including using a ruler to draw and measure lines to the nearest centimetre, recording estimates and measurements as '3 and a bit metres long' or 'about 8 centimetres' or 'nearly 3 kilograms heavy'.**
- Use and begin to read the vocabulary related to time.
  Use units of time and know the relationships between them (second, minute, hour, day, week).
  Suggest suitable units to estimate or measure time.
  Order the months of the year.
  Read the time to the hour, half hour or quarter hour on an analogue clock and a 12-hour digital clock, and understand the notation 7:30.

Teacher note

- Children need to have practical experience of these units in order to understand them fully.
- Children will require a ruler for this assessment.

Answers

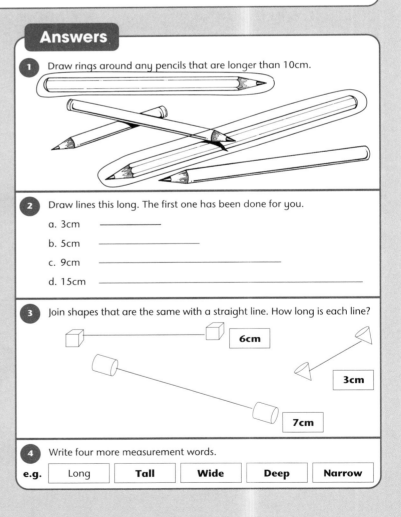

1 Draw rings around any pencils that are longer than 10cm.

2 Draw lines this long. The first one has been done for you.

a. 3cm ——————

b. 5cm ————————

c. 9cm ——————————————

d. 15cm ————————————————————————

3 Join shapes that are the same with a straight line. How long is each line?

6cm

3cm

7cm

4 Write four more measurement words.

e.g. | Long | **Tall** | **Wide** | **Deep** | **Narrow** |

ASSESSMENT 28

Measures

1 Draw rings around any pencils that are longer than 10cm.

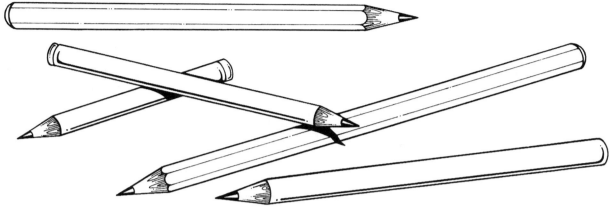

2 Draw lines this long. The first one has been done for you.

a. 3cm   _____

b. 5cm

c. 9cm

d. 15cm

3 Join shapes that are the same with a straight line. How long is each line?

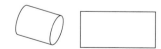

4 Write four more measurement words.

| Long | | | | |

Measures

Activity sheet questions

- Use and begin to read the vocabulary related to length, mass and capacity.
- Estimate, measure and compare lengths, masses and capacities, using standard units (m, cm, kg, litre); suggest suitable units and equipment for such measurements.
- Read a simple scale to the nearest labelled division, including using a ruler to draw and measure lines to the nearest centimetre, recording estimates and measurements as '3 and a bit metres long' or 'about 8 centimetres' or 'nearly 3 kilograms heavy'.

Written

All ● Use and begin to read the vocabulary related to time.

1 Order the months of the year.

2 Use units of time and know the relationships between them (second, minute, hour, day, week).

3–6 Suggest suitable units to estimate or measure time.

Read the time to the hour, half hour or quarter hour on an analogue clock and a 12-hour digital clock, and understand the notation 7:30.

Teacher note

- Children need experience in three aspects of time:
  1. **sequence** – becoming confident about the order in which time events take place
  2. **duration** – having a sense of the length of units of time
  3. **telling the time** – reading both digital and analogue clocks.
- Many children are able to 'read' digital time without having any real sense of what that time represents. This assessment mainly focuses on the duration aspect of time.

Answers

1 Fill in the gaps.

January, **February**, March, **April**, **May**, June, **July**, August, **September**, **October**, November, **December**.

2 a. 1 week = **7** days   c. 1 day = **24** hours

b. 1 hour = **60** minutes   d. 1 minute = **60** seconds

3 Tick the correct answer.
I would measure the time I take to travel to school in:

days ☐   hours ☐   minutes ✓   seconds ☐

4 Tick the correct answer.
I would measure the time I am in school each day in:

weeks ☐   days ☐   hours ✓   minutes ☐   seconds ☐

5 Write something that takes about:

a. 1 hour   **e.g. Lunch break**

b. 1 minute   **e.g. The music at the start of a TV programme**

c. 10 seconds   **e.g. Putting my coat on**

6 How long do you think:

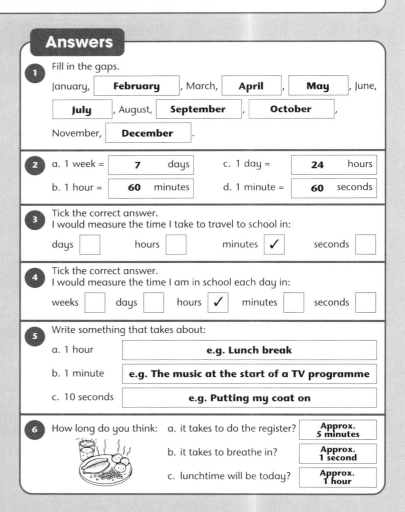

a. it takes to do the register?   **Approx. 5 minutes**

b. it takes to breathe in?   **Approx. 1 second**

c. lunchtime will be today?   **Approx. 1 hour**

ASSESSMENT 29

Measures

1 Fill in the gaps.

January, [_____], March, [_____], [_____], June,

[_____], August, [_____], [_____],

November, [_____].

2 a. 1 week = [_____] days   c. 1 day = [_____] hours

b. 1 hour = [_____] minutes   d. 1 minute = [_____] seconds

3 Tick the correct answer.
I would measure the time I take to travel to school in:

days [ ]   hours [ ]   minutes [ ]   seconds [ ]

4 Tick the correct answer.
I would measure the time I am in school each day in:

weeks [ ]   days [ ]   hours [ ]   minutes [ ]   seconds [ ]

5 Write something that takes about:

a. 1 hour   [_____]

b. 1 minute   [_____]

c. 10 seconds   [_____]

6 How long do you think: a. it takes to do the register?   [_____]

b. it takes to breathe in?   [_____]

c. lunchtime will be today?   [_____]

Measures

Activity sheet questions

- Use and begin to read the vocabulary related to length, mass and capacity.
- Estimate, measure and compare lengths, masses and capacities, using standard units (m, cm, kg, litre); suggest suitable units and equipment for such measurements.
- Read a simple scale to the nearest labelled division, including using a ruler to draw and measure lines to the nearest centimetre, recording estimates and measurements as '3 and a bit metres long' or 'about 8 centimetres' or 'nearly 3 kilograms heavy'.
- Use and begin to read the vocabulary related to time.
  Use units of time and know the relationships between them (second, minute, hour, day, week).
  Suggest suitable units to estimate or measure time.
  Order the months of the year.

Written
1–4
- **Read the time to the hour, half hour or quarter hour on an analogue clock and a 12-hour digital clock, and understand the notation 7:30.**

Teacher note

- Children need experience in three aspects of time:
  1. **sequence** – becoming confident about the order in which time events take place
  2. **duration** – having a sense of the length of units of time
  3. **telling the time** – reading both digital and analogue clocks.
- Many children are able to 'read' digital time without having any real sense of what that time represents. This assessment mainly focuses on the duration aspect of time.

Answers

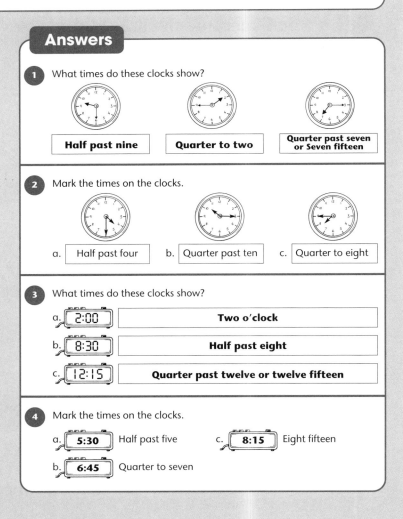

1 What times do these clocks show?

| Half past nine | Quarter to two | Quarter past seven or Seven fifteen |

2 Mark the times on the clocks.

a. Half past four   b. Quarter past ten   c. Quarter to eight

3 What times do these clocks show?

a. 2:00 — Two o'clock
b. 8:30 — Half past eight
c. 12:15 — Quarter past twelve or twelve fifteen

4 Mark the times on the clocks.

a. 5:30 Half past five   c. 8:15 Eight fifteen
b. 6:45 Quarter to seven

Name: _____ Date: _____

1 What times do these clocks show?

2 Mark the times on the clocks.

a. | Half past four | b. | Quarter past ten | c. | Quarter to eight |

3 What times do these clocks show?

a. 2:00 _____

b. 8:30 _____

c. 12:15 _____

4 Mark the times on the clocks.

a.  Half past five   c.  Eight fifteen

b. Quarter to seven

Activity sheet questions

Written

1–2
- Use the mathematical names for common 3D shapes, including the pyramid, cylinder … .
  Relate solid shapes to pictures of them.

3–4
Sort shapes and describe some of their features, such as the shapes of faces and number of faces, edges and corners (3D shapes).

- Begin to recognise line symmetry.
- Use mathematical vocabulary to describe position, direction and movement: for example, describe, place, tick, draw or visualise objects in given positions.
- Recognise whole, half and quarter turns, to the left or right, clockwise or anti-clockwise.
  Know that a right angle is a measure of a quarter turn, and recognise right angles in squares and rectangles.

Teacher note

- Children need to appreciate that shapes can be in different orientations. They need access to solid shapes, without which they may think that a cube, for example, has only 9 edges because of how it appears in a 2D picture.

Answers

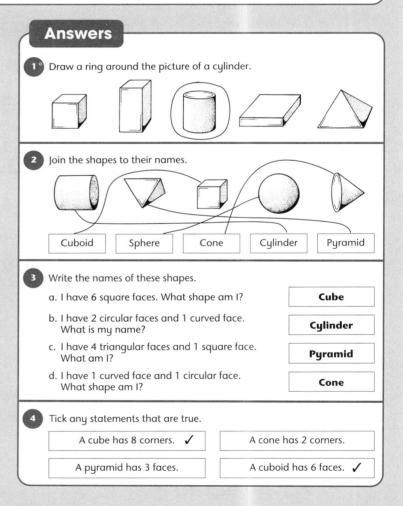

Name: _____   Date: _____

1 Draw a ring around the picture of a cylinder.

2 Join the shapes to their names.

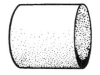

| Cuboid | Sphere | Cone | Cylinder | Pyramid |

3 Write the names of these shapes.

a. I have 6 square faces. What shape am I?

b. I have 2 circular faces and 1 curved face. What is my name?

c. I have 4 triangular faces and 1 square face. What am I?

d. I have 1 curved face and 1 circular face. What shape am I?

4 Tick any statements that are true.

| A cube has 8 corners. | A cone has 2 corners. |
| A pyramid has 3 faces. | A cuboid has 6 faces. |

Shape and space – 2D

Activity sheet questions

Written

1–2 • Use the mathematical names for common 2D shapes, including the pentagon, hexagon, octagon … .

3–4 **Sort shapes and describe some of their features, such as the number of sides and corners, symmetry (2D shapes).**

• Begin to recognise line symmetry.

• Use mathematical vocabulary to describe position, direction and movement: for example, describe, place, tick, draw or visualise objects in given positions.

• Recognise whole, half and quarter turns, to the left or right, clockwise or anti-clockwise.
Know that a right angle is a measure of a quarter turn, and recognise right angles in squares and rectangles.

Teacher note

• Children need experience of shapes in different orientations. They sometimes believe that triangles must have a horizontal base, for example.

Answers

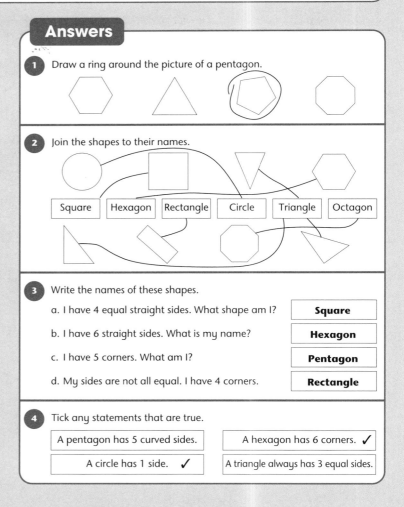

1 Draw a ring around the picture of a pentagon.

2 Join the shapes to their names.

Square | Hexagon | Rectangle | Circle | Triangle | Octagon

3 Write the names of these shapes.

a. I have 4 equal straight sides. What shape am I? **Square**

b. I have 6 straight sides. What is my name? **Hexagon**

c. I have 5 corners. What am I? **Pentagon**

d. My sides are not all equal. I have 4 corners. **Rectangle**

4 Tick any statements that are true.

A pentagon has 5 curved sides. | A hexagon has 6 corners. ✓

A circle has 1 side. ✓ | A triangle always has 3 equal sides.

Name: _____   Date: _____

Shape and space – 2D

1 Draw a ring around the picture of a pentagon.

2 Join the shapes to their names.

Square	Hexagon	Rectangle	Circle	Triangle	Octagon

3 Write the names of these shapes.

a. I have 4 equal straight sides. What shape am I?

b. I have 6 straight sides. What is my name?

c. I have 5 corners. What am I?

d. My sides are not all equal. I have 4 corners.

4 Tick any statements that are true.

A pentagon has 5 curved sides.	A hexagon has 6 corners.
A circle has 1 side.	A triangle always has 3 equal sides.

Shape and space

Activity sheet questions

- Use the mathematical names for common 3D and 2D shapes, including the pyramid, cylinder, pentagon, hexagon, octagon … .
  Sort shapes and describe some of their features, such as the number of sides and corners, symmetry (2D shapes), or the shapes of faces and number of faces, edges and corners (3D shapes).
  Relate solid shapes to pictures of them.

Written

1–2
- **Begin to recognise line symmetry.**

3
- **Use mathematical vocabulary to describe position, direction and movement: for example, describe, place, tick, draw or visualise objects in given positions.**
- Recognise whole, half and quarter turns, to the left or right, clockwise or anti-clockwise.
  Know that a right angle is a measure of a quarter turn, and recognise right angles in squares and rectangles.

Teacher note

- Provide mirrors and tracing paper to assist in checking for lines of symmetry.

Answers

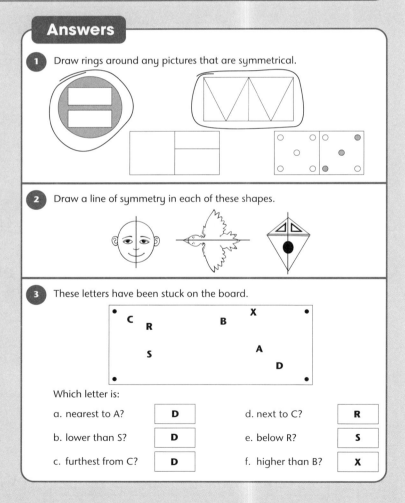

1. Draw rings around any pictures that are symmetrical.

2. Draw a line of symmetry in each of these shapes.

3. These letters have been stuck on the board.

Which letter is:

a. nearest to A?	**D**		d. next to C?	**R**
b. lower than S?	**D**		e. below R?	**S**
c. furthest from C?	**D**		f. higher than B?	**X**

Shape and space

1 Draw rings around any pictures that are symmetrical.

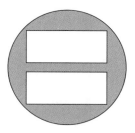

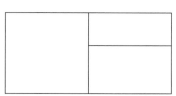
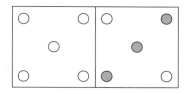

2 Draw a line of symmetry in each of these shapes.

3 These letters have been stuck on the board.

C
R
X
B
S
A
D

Which letter is:

a. nearest to A?

d. next to C?

b. lower than S?

e. below R?

c. furthest from C?

f. higher than B?

MATHS WEEKLY ASSESSMENT: *Book 2*

Shape and space

Activity sheet questions

- Use the mathematical names for common 3D and 2D shapes, including the pyramid, cylinder, pentagon, hexagon, octagon … .
  Sort shapes and describe some of their features, such as the number of sides and corners, symmetry (2D shapes), or the shapes of faces and number of faces, edges and corners (3D shapes).
  Relate solid shapes to pictures of them.
- Begin to recognise line symmetry.
- Use mathematical vocabulary to describe position, direction and movement: for example, describe, place, tick, draw or visualise objects in given positions.

Written

1–2
- **Recognise whole, half and quarter turns, to the left or right, clockwise or anti-clockwise.**

3
  Know that a right angle is a measure of a quarter turn, and recognise right angles in squares and rectangles.

Teacher note

- Provide opportunities in PE, for example, for children to experience whole, half and quarter turns. Relate right angles to the world around children by pointing out examples in the classroom.

Answers

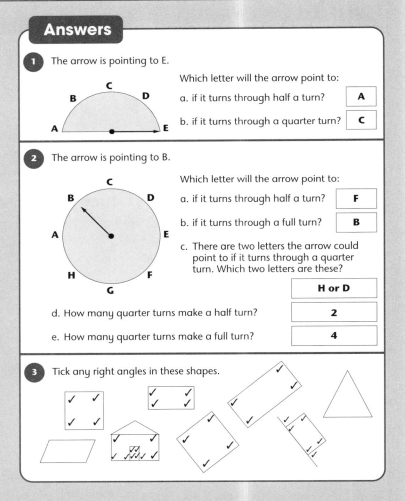

1 The arrow is pointing to E.

Which letter will the arrow point to:

a. if it turns through half a turn? **A**

b. if it turns through a quarter turn? **C**

2 The arrow is pointing to B.

Which letter will the arrow point to:

a. if it turns through half a turn? **F**

b. if it turns through a full turn? **B**

c. There are two letters the arrow could point to if it turns through a quarter turn. Which two letters are these?

H or D

d. How many quarter turns make a half turn? **2**

e. How many quarter turns make a full turn? **4**

3 Tick any right angles in these shapes.

Name: _____   Date: _____

1 The arrow is pointing to E.

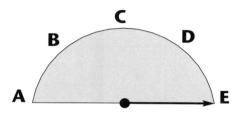

Which letter will the arrow point to:

a. if it turns through half a turn?

b. if it turns through a quarter turn?

2 The arrow is pointing to B.

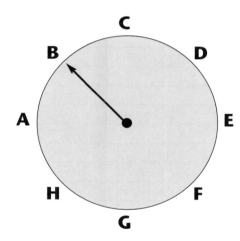

Which letter will the arrow point to:

a. if it turns through half a turn?

b. if it turns through a full turn?

c. There are two letters the arrow could point to if it turns through a quarter turn. Which two letters are these?

d. How many quarter turns make a half turn?

e. How many quarter turns make a full turn?

3 Tick any right angles in these shapes.

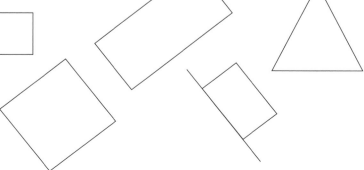

Record sheet

Number of answers

Names	Assessment No.	1	2	3	4	5	6	7	8	9	10	11	12	13	14	15	16	17	18	19	20	21	22	23	24	25	26	27	28	29	30	31	32	33	34